Contents

Introduction

Abacus Foundation

Since the introduction of the Foundation Stage and the publication of the related *Curriculum Guidance* in May 2000, teachers in playgroups, nurseries and reception classes now have both curriculum content and a set of principles to inform their teaching. The *Curriculum Guidance for the Foundation Stage* designates six areas of learning for children, one of which is 'Mathematical development'. Each area is outlined in some detail and provides a series of 'stepping stones'. These are intended to help practitioners plan a progression of activities to allow children to achieve the Early Learning Goals.

The **Abacus Foundation** materials are designed and written to support teachers with planning and teaching to match the *Curriculum Guidance for the Foundation Stage*. Two books are provided at each level (F1 for 3- to 4-year-olds, F2 for 4- to 5-year-olds) – a Teachers' Resource Book and an Activity Book. The Teachers' Resource Book comprises a complete series of weekly plans which include suggestions for daily 'on- the -rug' large group teacher-led activities, and outlines of differentiated ideas for teacher-initiated small group or paired activities (these are expanded in detail in the Activity Book), as well as opportunities for learning through structured play activities.

The weekly plans in the Teachers' Resource Book, backed up by the bank of activities in the Activity Book, save teachers time by offering a balanced and adaptable starting point, and allow them to cease re-inventing the wheel by continually writing their own material. The plans are linked to the 'Mathematical development' strand in the *Curriculum Guidance for the Foundation Stage* and provide a comprehensive two-year programme leading clearly to the Early Learning Goals for mathematics.

Activity Book

The **Abacus Foundation** Activity Books for F1 and F2 are an ideal resource for all those working with children aged 3 to 5. The activities can be used in school, in a playgroup or nursery, or even at home. Some are suitable for more direct or formal teaching, and others will slot effectively into the context of a play activity. Most of the activities can be used either with one child, pairs or groups of up to five children. The weekly activities are differentiated to enable teachers to plan efficiently, and any practitioner to select appropriate activities for different children. All the activities in this large bank are flexible and can easily be adapted to accommodate a range of specific circumstances, making this book a perfect dip-in resource to reinforce children's mathematical skills as they learn.

The activities in this book are provided in two sections – differentiated activities linked directly to the weekly plans in the Teachers' Resource Book, followed by a bank of further activities arranged by mathematical topic. The Activity Book can be used in a variety of ways:
- to find an activity for immediate use
- to plan activities for the next half term in conjunction with the weekly plans in the Teachers' Resource Book
- to provide an activity for parents and children to share – either at home or in school
- to select activities by topic linked to the Early Learning Goals.

The differentiated activities, ordered by term and week, are outlined in brief on the matching weekly plans, then expanded in more detail in this book. They give suggestions for Easy, Medium and Hard activities to match the objectives of each weekly plan. This enables teachers to select activities to suit particular groups of children and also to plan a progression of activities throughout the year.

The activities are intended for use in a teaching situation, when a practitioner is working with a small group on a teacher-initiated activity, but some are also appropriate for more informal learning situations where the children are engaged in play activities and choose what to do themselves. The majority of the activities need little preparation and are suitable for learning support assistants or parents to use within or outside the classroom context. Each activity includes the following information:

- Learning points to assist the practitioner in directing the children and making informal assessments. In the case of the differentiated activities, these learning points draw directly on the objectives from the appropriate weekly plan.
- A list of materials required for the activity. It is likely that most of these will be freely available in the classroom ensuring that prior preparation time is kept to a minimum.
- Detailed instructions on how to run the activity, including suggestions for questions to ask the children.

Classroom management

Good early years practice involves the setting up of a wide variety of informal learning situations, and also some direct teaching in several different contexts. Play is crucial, but so is demonstrating or modelling how to do something. Young children's development relies upon the regular supply of a varied diet of educational activity. The most successful – and also the most appealing – educational settings are those which provide both free play as well as short sessions of direct teaching. 'On the rug' time or 'Circle time' of teacher-led activities with a large group, or teacher-initiated activities with a small group, allow teachers to demonstrate particular skills very effectively. Equally, becoming an 'expert play partner' helps the practitioner offer specific learning opportunities for children, e.g. recognising colours or comparing and sorting when playing in the water tray or sand pit. In any of these contexts, children will learn not only the maths in question, but also how to persevere, concentrate and work with others.

In accordance with the principles of the *Curriculum Guidance for the Foundation Stage*, the **Abacus Foundation** materials allow for children to be taught and learn in a variety of contexts. Some areas of mathematics are best taught directly, to a large group. Others are better suited to teaching a small group, and some skills, such as writing numerals, require attention on an individual level. A variety of all these teaching – and learning – methods can be used at different times for most skills. Some, however, cannot be directly taught, and are best acquired in the course of an informal activity, i.e. a structured play activity that is initiated or led by the child.

The following table categorises the mathematical skills covered in the Foundation Stage into suitable learning situations.

	Large group	Small group	Individuals or pairs
Taught directly	• Counting • Chanting number names in order • Counting objects/ events/movements • Number rhymes • Days of the week • Shape names	• Counting objects • Matching a spoken numeral to quantity • Adding 1 or 2 more • Partitioning a set • Comparing lengths	• Matching numerals to sets • Writing numerals • Matching days of the week to special events
Learned informally	• Sorting shapes • Colours • Recognising large numbers • Positions		

Term 1

Week 1

On track
Easy

- *Counting to 6*
- *Using a number track*

Number track (1 to 6), a coin, counters

The children each place their counter on number 1 on the track. They take turns to spin a coin and move accordingly: heads move forwards one place, tails move backwards one place (apart from on number 1, where they miss a turn). The children say the number of the space they move to. The first child to reach number 6 wins.

Stop and clap
Medium

- *Counting to 6*
- *Using a number track*

Number track (1 to 6), counters

The children place their counter on number 1 on the track. In turn, they move along the track, choosing where to stop. They say the number and then do the same number of jumps or claps. Let them do this several times.

Reaching the end
Hard

- *Counting to 6*
- *Using a number track*

Number track (1 to 10), a coin, counters

The children each place their counter on number 1 on the track. They take turns to spin the coin: heads move forwards one, tails move forwards two. Encourage the children to say which number they land on. If they are correct, they leave the counter there, otherwise move it to the original space. They continue until one child's counter reaches 10.

Week 2

Space fillers
Easy

- *Counting up to 4 objects*

Grids with different-sized cells (2 x 2)

Show the children the grids and ask them to find groups of four objects in the room, e.g. four bricks, that will fit on the grid. *These spaces are bigger. Can you find four large things to fit on this grid?* Take away one of the objects. *How many are on the grid now?* Repeat.

Grid totals
Medium

• *Counting up to 6 objects*
Different grids (1 x 3, 2 x 2, 1 x 5, 2 x 3), beads
Give each group a grid of an appropriate size. Ask the children to put a small object, e.g. a bead, in each cell and count the total. Give them a different grid and ask them to repeat the exercise.

Collecting bricks
Hard

• *Counting more than 6 objects*
A dice, building bricks
Taking turns, the children roll the dice and count the spots. If they are correct, they collect that number of building bricks. After several turns each, encourage the children to count the total number of bricks they have and build a model with them. *Who has collected the most bricks?*

Week 3

Circle or square?
Easy

• *Matching similar 2-d shapes*
• *Recognising squares and circles*
A feely bag, various different-sized 2-d shapes including squares and circles, a large piece of paper
Draw a circle and a square on a large sheet of paper. Place the shapes in the bag and let a child take one out. Ask them to identify the shape and place it in either the circle or the square on the paper, as appropriate. Shapes that are neither squares nor circles should be placed outside the shapes on the paper. Continue until the bag is empty.

A shape picture
Medium

• *Recognising squares, circles and triangles*
Plastic or cardboard 2-d squares and circles
Give the children a variety of different-sized squares and circles and ask them to create a shape picture with them. When their picture is complete, the children count how many of each shape they have used.

Shape patterns
Hard

• *Matching similar 2-d shapes*
• *Recognising squares, circles and triangles*
Plastic or cardboard 2-d shapes
Give each child a shape. Explain that they are going to line up to create a pattern with their shapes. Ask a child holding a square to stand at the beginning of the line, then ask a child with a triangle to stand next in line. Continue until all the children are included. Ask the children to say the pattern with you as you point to each shape. *Square, triangle, circle, square, triangle, circle, ...* Then let the children suggest a different pattern. *Square, square, circle, circle, square, square, circle, circle, ...*

Week 4

Our house
Easy

• *Adding one more to a small set*
Drawings of houses, paper doll outlines, glue
Give each child an outline of a house and ask them to pretend that it is their house. Give the children a paper doll for every member of their family and ask them to draw on their faces, clothes and so on. They then glue the dolls onto the house, count the number of people and write the number by the house. Now explain that someone else is arriving to live with them, perhaps granny or a new baby. Let them colour another doll and add it to the house. *How many people are living at the house now?*

Another cube
Medium

• *Adding one more to a small set*
A dice, interlocking cubes
The children roll the dice in turn. They count the number of spots and take that number of cubes. *How many cubes do you have?* They then add one more cube. *How many cubes do you have now?* Repeat several times.

Bricks and bricks
Hard

• *Increasing a set by one or two*
A numbered dice (1 to 6), building bricks
Roll the dice and say the number. The children take that many bricks. Ask them to take two more bricks. *How many bricks do you have now?* Encourage them to say the calculation. *Five and two make seven.* Repeat several times.

Week 5

Ducks on a pond
Easy

• *Rearranging objects to show that there are still the same number*
A bowl of water, five plastic ducks, number cards (several 5 cards)
Ask the children to count the ducks as a child puts them into the bowl one by one. *How many ducks are on the pond? How do you know?* Give the children a 5 number card. *This is the number of ducks in the pond. Oliver, can you stir the water? How many ducks are there now?* Ask the children to show the number card. Explain that they do not need to change the number card unless a duck is added to or removed from the pond. You may need to take the ducks out and recount.

Dice roll
Medium

• *Rearranging objects to show that there are still the same number*
A large dice, interlocking cubes
Roll the dice. The children count the spots and each child takes that number of cubes, all in different colours. Ask them to count the cubes in unison. *How many cubes in your pile, Harry?* Check that each child has the same number of cubes. Ask the children to make a line or a pattern with their cubes which is different from their neighbour's. *How many cubes do you have in front of you? Did anyone know without counting?* Repeat several times.

How many bricks?
Hard

• *Rearranging objects to show that there are still the same number*
Number cards (1 to 10), building bricks
Shuffle the cards and place them face down in a pile. The children each take a card and the same number of bricks. They count the bricks and make a line with them. Rearrange the bricks. *How many bricks are there now? Do you still have the same number?* Repeat several times.

Week 6

Our zoo
Easy

• *Comparing objects by size*
Three large sheets of paper, paint, paintbrushes
Ask the children to think of a tall, a medium-sized and a short animal. Together, paint each animal on a sheet of paper, bearing in mind their proportions, and display them alongside each other. Look at the animals and discuss their sizes. *Which animal is taller than two others?*

Looking at leaves
Medium

• *Comparing objects by size*
Different-sized leaves
Show the children the leaves. Ask them to order them in size, from the smallest to largest. As they work, talk about the sizes of the leaves. *How do you know that this one should go there? Which is the smallest leaf? Which is the largest?*

Animal kingdom
Hard

• *Comparing objects by size*
Pictures of animals
Show the children a variety of animal pictures. Talk about which animals are tall, which are medium-sized and which are short. *How do you know that this is a tall animal?* Group the pictures according to the size of the animals. Then ask each child to draw a picture of a tall, a medium-sized and a short animal.

Week 7

Shoe bags
Easy

• *Comparing objects by weight*
Several pairs of shoes, two identical bags
Let the children examine the shoes by feeling how heavy they are individually. Explain that although they are similar, their weights are different. Ask the children to place pairs of shoes into the two bags to make a heavy set of shoes and a light set. Let them each hold the bags to feel their weight. *Which bag is heavier?* Repeat with different pairs of shoes.

Can you lift it?
Medium

• *Sorting into 'too heavy to pick up' and 'light enough to pick up'*
Pictures cut from a catalogue (different types of cars, bicycles, prams, shopping trolleys or baskets, scooters)
Spread the pictures on the floor and ask the children to choose a picture of something that they could not pick up. *Why couldn't Jack pick up the car? It is too heavy.* Repeat with other pictures. Sort the pictures into two sets: those showing objects that are too heavy to pick up and those that are light enough to pick up.

My weight
Hard

• *Comparing objects by weight*
Ask the children to draw a picture of themselves in the middle of a sheet of paper. *Can you find something in the classroom that is heavier than you? How do you know it is heavier than you?* Ask them to draw that object next to their self-portrait. *Can you see something that is lighter than you?* Ask them to draw that object on the other side of their self-portrait. *How do you know that it is lighter than you?* Ask the children to name some other objects heavier and lighter than themselves.

Week 8

Ten beads
Easy

• *Estimating a number*
Beads, string
Let each child count out 10 beads and consider what that number of beads looks and feels like. They then thread them onto a piece of string and count them again. Take a handful of beads and show them to the children. Ask the children to estimate the number, without counting them. The child with the nearest estimate keeps a bead and adds it to their string. Repeat several times. Who has the longest string of beads? That child wins.

Brick mugs
Medium

• *Estimating a number*
Small building bricks, a mug
Ask each child to take 20 bricks and consider what they look and feel like. Fill a mug with some bricks. *How many bricks do you think are in the mug?* Encourage the children to think about their piles of 20 bricks to help them. Tip the bricks out of the mug and count them in tens. The child with the closest guess wins. Repeat several times.

Two numbers
Hard

• *Talking about big and small numbers*
Number cards (1 to 100), a number grid (1 to 100), interlocking cubes
Shuffle the cards and place them face down in a pile. Ask each child to take a card, say their number and find it on the grid. *Who has the largest number?* That child takes a cube. Continue until all the cards have been taken. *Who has the most cubes?*

Week 9

Cards and coins
Easy

• *Recognising numbers to 6*
A dice, 1p coins, number cards (1 to 6)
Give each child a set of number cards. In turn, the children roll the dice, count the spots and take that number of 1p coins. They then find the matching number card and place the coins on it in the same arrangement as the spots on the dice. They continue until all of their cards are matched with coins.

Cards and beads
Medium

• *Recognising numbers to 6*

A feely bag, number cards (1 to 6), beads

Give each child a set of number cards and ask them to place them face up, in order, in front of them. Place up to six beads in the bag. Pass the bag around to each child in turn and ask them to feel the beads and to choose a number card to match the number of beads. When they have all done this, tip out the beads and count them together. *Who has correctly found card two?* Those children turn over their card. Repeat until one child has turned over all of their cards.

Coin matches
Hard

• *Recognising numbers to 6*

A numbered dice (1 to 6), 1p coins, number cards (1 to 6)

Give each child a set of number cards. In turn, the children roll the dice, say the number and find that number of coins. They find the same number card and place the coins on it. Continue until all the children have matched their cards to the same number of coins.

Week 10

Disappearing act
Easy

• *Matching similar 3-d shapes*

3-d shapes (cubes, spheres, cylinders), a tray

Arrange several 3-d shapes on a tray and leave one of each type on the table. Let the children look at the shapes on the tray and identify what each one is. Ask them to shut their eyes while you remove one of the shapes from the tray. *The shape I have taken away has six straight sides. Which one is it?* Ask the children to point to the correct shape on the table. Show them if they were correct or not. Repeat several times. Let the children remove one of the shapes and describe it.

What's in the bag?
Medium

• *Recognising shapes*

3-d shapes, a feely bag

Use a selection of 3-d shapes and display an example of each on the table. Without the children seeing, place a shape in the bag and pass the bag to a child to feel. *Which shape is in the bag? Can you point to a similar one on the table?* Repeat several times.

Missing shapes
Hard

• *Recognising shapes*

3-d shapes (cubes, spheres, cylinders, cuboids, cones), a feely bag

Place an example of each shape in the bag and display an example of each on the table. Pass the bag round to each child to feel the shapes in the bag. Secretly remove one of the shapes from the bag. *Which shape have I taken out of the bag?* Encourage the children to ask you questions about the shapes to find out which one is missing. *Yes, I have taken out the cylinder. Can you show me another cylinder on the table?*

Week 11

Garden centre
Easy

• *Recognising that we use coins for buying and selling*

Flowers, plants, coins (1p, 2p, 5p, 10p), price labels ('1p', '2p', '5p','10p')

Set up a 'garden centre' in the role play area. Give each child a selection of coins. Price the flowers and plants and ask the children to help you read the prices. *How much is this bunch of flowers? Hold up the correct coin to buy the bunch of flowers.* In turn, let the children buy something at the garden centre. Explain that they must offer the correct coin and that they are not given any change. If they offer the wrong coin, they must wait until their next turn to try again.

Coin tracks
Medium

• *Recognising coins*
• *Ordering coins*

Real coins (1p, 2p, 5p, 10p, 20p, 50p), Blu-tack

Give each child a selection of coins and ask them to line them up in order of value, from the least to the most. Let them secure the coins to the table with Blu-tack to make a long track. How many of each coin do they have?

What can you buy?
Hard

- *Recognising that we use coins for buying and selling*

Real and plastic coins (1p, 2p, 5p, 10p, 20p, 50p), long pieces of card, sticky tape

Show the children the real coins and ask them what they could buy with one of each. *Could you buy a book with this two pence coin?* Fold the sheets of card to make zig-zag books. Ask the children to stick a plastic coin of different value on each page. Next to each coin, the children can then draw an item they could buy with that coin.

Week 12

Day and night
Easy

- *Talking about day and night*
- *Recognising the difference between day and night*

Pictures of objects and animals associated with day and night

Discuss the differences between day and night with the help of pictures such as a bed, an owl, the moon, toys, etc. Talk about animals that are seen mainly at night. *What things do we use just before we go to bed?* Ask the children to sort the pictures into two piles, one for day and one for night.

Bedtime tantrums!
Medium

- *Talking about day and night*
- *Recognising the difference between day and night*

Ask the children how they feel about going to bed at night. *Do you go to bed as soon as your mummy and daddy tell you or do you find something else to do instead? Have you ever done anything naughty at bedtime?* Talk about why we need to go to bed. Ask the children to imagine what a naughty child might do at bedtime. Collect lots of ideas and let the children act out the scenario, taking different roles such as the child, parents, or babysitter.

Midnight and midday
Hard

- *Talking about day and night*
- *Recognising the difference between day and night*

Pictures of day- and night-time scenes, labels ('midnight', 'midday'), glue

Explain the meanings of midnight and midday and show the children the labels. Let them look at the pictures of different times of the day and sort them under the two labels. The children can then glue the pictures to make a midnight poster and a midday poster.

Week 13

A spot dice

Easy

• *Recognising numbers to 6*

A net of a cube, a large dice, sticky tape

Give each child a net of a cube and ask them to make their own dice. Help them to fold along the edges and attach the tape. Encourage them to draw the spots on each face of the dice, pointing out that the total of spots on opposite sides is 7. Ensure that they draw the spots in the same patterns as on the large dice.

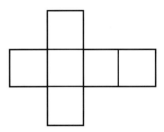

Number frieze

Medium

• *Recognising numbers to 6*

Long sheets of paper divided and numbered into 10 segments

Give each child a sheet of paper and ask them to draw items related to themselves in each numbered segment. For example, they could draw three cats in box 3, ten toes in box 10, or two sisters in box 2.

A decorated track

Hard

• *Recognising numbers*

Number tracks (1 to 20), a dice, counters

Give each child a number track and ask them to decorate it by drawing in numbers of small items, according to the number of each segment, e.g. six eggs in 6 or eight worms in 8. Taking turns, the children roll the dice and move that many sections along the track. As they land on each section, they clap or jump that many times. The children continue until they reach the end of the track.

Term 2

Week 1

Keeping track
Easy

- *Counting to 6*
- *Using a number track*

Number tracks (1 to 6), counters (in two colours), a dice

Playing in pairs, the children take turns to roll the dice. They count the number of spots rolled and count that number along the number track. They place one of their counters on that space. They continue until one of them has placed a counter on every space.

Tracking to 10
Medium

- *Counting to 10*
- *Using a number track*

Number track (1 to 10), counters (in different colours)

The children take turns to choose, in secret, a number on the number track and clap that many times. The rest of the group counts the claps and says the number. If correct, the child who clapped puts one of their counters on that number on the track. The children continue until each number has at least one counter on it. *Who has the most counters on the track?*

Tracking to 20
Hard

- *Counting to 20*
- *Using a number track*

Number tracks (1 to 20), coins, counters

In pairs, the children place a counter on number 1 on the track. They toss the coin: heads move forwards one, tails move forwards two. Encourage the children to say which number they land on and to count on from the previous number. If correct, the counter stays there, otherwise, they move it back two spaces. They continue until they reach 20. Extend the children by putting in some hazards on the track, e.g. if you land on 6 you miss a turn.

Week 2

Six spaces
Easy

- *Counting up to 6 objects*

Grids with different-sized cells (2 x 3)

Show the children the grids and ask them to find groups of six objects in the room, e.g. six toy cars, that will fit on the grid. *These spaces are bigger. Can you find six large things to fit on this grid?* Take away one of the objects. *How many are on the grid now?* Repeat.

Fill the grid
Medium

- *Counting up to 10 objects*

Different grids (1 x 5, 1 x 7, 2 x 3, 2 x 5, 3 x 3, 4 x 2), interlocking cubes

Give each group a grid of an appropriate size. Ask the children to put a small object, e.g. a cube, in each cell and to count the total. Give them a different grid and ask them to repeat the exercise.

Brick models
Hard

• *Recognising numbers to 10*
A ten-sided dice (1 to 10), building bricks
In turn, the children roll the dice and say the number out loud. If correct, they collect that number of building bricks. Repeat several times. Encourage the children to count their total number of bricks and build a model with them. *Who has collected the most bricks?*

Week 3

Find it!
Easy

• *Beginning to use the language of position*
A doll's house and dolls, or a garage and toy cars
Ask the children to shut their eyes while you hide a doll or a car in the house or garage. Using positional language, tell the children where it is hidden. *The doll is hiding inside the cupboard.* Taking turns, let one of the children find the doll. Can they go straight to it? Repeat several times. Let the children take turns to hide the doll or car and to describe its position.

Placing the animals
Medium

• *Beginning to use the language of position*
Toy animals, a small box
Let one of the children take an animal and say a position, e.g. *Above.* Another child then takes the animal and places it in that position in relation to the box. Continue until all the animals have been positioned. Say a position, e.g. *Underneath.* The children have to say which animal is in this position. If they are correct, let them take the animal. Continue until all the animals have been collected.

In the house
Hard

• *Beginning to use the language of position*
A large picture of a house, adhesive cartoon characters, small cards with positional language
Show the children the picture of the house. The children take turns to choose one of the cards. Read the position for them and ask them to place a cartoon character in that position in the house. Continue until all the cards have been used. Ask questions and encourage the children to describe the position of each character.

Week 4

Beads on a string
Easy

• *Increasing a set by one or two*
Beads, pieces of string (knotted at one end), a dice
Roll the dice and ask one of the children to say the number. Tell the children to thread that number of beads onto a piece of string. *How many beads are on your string? Can you count the beads so that I know you are right? How many beads will there be if you thread one more onto your string?* Then ask them to thread two more beads onto the string and to check the new total.

A peg hanger
Medium

• *Understanding that adding is increasing a set by a given number*
• *Increasing a set by one or two*
A wire coat hanger, clothes pegs
Let each child clip a clothes peg onto the coat hanger. *How many pegs are on the hanger?* Invite a child to add another peg. *How many pegs are on the hanger now?* Repeat several times, sometimes asking the children to add two more pegs.

More bricks
Hard

• *Increasing a set by one or two*
A ten-sided dice (1 to 10), building bricks
Roll the dice and say the number. The children take that many bricks. Ask them to take two more bricks. *How many bricks do you have now?* Encourage them to say the calculation. *Eight and two make ten.* Repeat several times.

Week 5

Bead bag
Easy

• *Rearranging a set and partitioning in different ways*

Five beads, a transparent plastic bag, a needle and thread

Place the beads in the bag. Stitch the bag down the middle, leaving just enough space at the bottom to slip one bead at a time through to the other side of the bag. Start with five beads on one side of the bag. Push one bead through to the other side. Encourage the children to say the calculation. *Four and one make five.* Repeat. *Three and two make five.* Continue until you have covered all the possible combinations.

Red cube, yellow cube
Medium

• *Rearranging a set and partitioning in different ways*

Interlocking cubes (red and yellow)

Give each child some red and yellow cubes. Ask them to make a tower of five cubes using both colours. They should make as many different towers as they can. Looking at each possible combination, ask the children to count the number of red and yellow cubes in each tower and then say the calculation. *Three red cubes and two yellow cubes make five cubes. Four red cubes and one yellow cube make five cubes.*

Penny cards
Hard

• *Rearranging a set and partitioning in different ways*

Number cards (1, 2, 3, 3, 4, 5, 6), 1p coins

Give each child a set of number cards and ask them to place them in a line with the 6 card in the middle. They then count out 1p coins onto each card to match the numeral. *How can we put two cards together so that there will be six one pence coins altogether?* Let the children match up all the possible pairs, using the coins to help them.

Week 6

Long tall animals
Easy

• *Comparing objects by size*
• *Distinguishing tall and long objects*

Pictures of long and tall animals, paint, paintbrushes

Show the children some pictures of long and tall animals, such as snakes and giraffes. Ask each child to paint a different animal and then display them in two sets, labelled 'long' and 'tall'.

On the road
Medium

- *Comparing objects by size*
- *Distinguishing tall and long objects*

Ask the children to think of long and tall vehicles that they see on the roads, e.g. a long coach, a tall bus, a long lorry and a tall tractor. Invite the children to draw as many different ones as they can think of. Display the pictures in two sets, labelled 'long' and 'tall'.

Tall and long
Hard

- *Comparing objects by size*
- *Distinguishing tall and long objects*

Let the children look around the classroom or the school to find three tall items. Ask them to draw one of them. Repeat for long items. Display their work under two headings, 'tall' and 'long'.

Week 7

Weighty bags
Easy

- *Comparing objects by weight*

Two identical bags, light and heavy objects

Without the children seeing, place a heavy object in one bag and a light one in the other. In turn, let the children compare the weight of the bags. *Can you say which bag is heavy and which is light?* Ask them if they can guess what is in each bag. Repeat with different objects.

Heavier than you?
Medium

- *Comparing objects by weight*

Ask the children to draw a picture of themselves in the middle of a sheet of paper. *Can you think of some things that are heavier than you?* Ask them to draw one object next to their self-portrait, e.g. a car. *Can you think of some things that are lighter than you?* Ask them to draw one object on the other side of their self-portrait. Ask the children to name some other objects heavier and lighter than themselves and to say why they think they are heavier or lighter.

Food weights
Hard

- *Comparing objects by weight*

A heavy cake

Encourage the children to think of some foods that are heavy, e.g. potatoes, fruit cake and tinned baked beans. Ask them to name some that are light, e.g. crisps, crackers and eggs. Discuss how heavy they are to pick up. *Which foods are easier to pick up than others?* Ask the children to draw a picture of their favourite heavy food. Bring in a heavy cake and let the children try it.

Week 8

A handful of cubes
Easy

• *Comparing two quantities*
Interlocking cubes
Working in pairs, each child counts out ten cubes and makes a tower with them. They then each take a new handful of cubes and estimate how many they have picked up. They make a new tower with the cubes, count them and compare the new tower with the tower of ten cubes. Were their estimates correct? *Who has the taller/shorter tower? Who has more/fewer cubes in their tower? Jon, how do you know that you have fewer cubes than Lizzie?*

A handful of bricks
Medium

• *Comparing two quantities*
• *Discussing who has less and who has more*
Small building bricks
Each child counts out 20 bricks. They handle them to appreciate what that amount of bricks looks and feels like. They then take a second handful of bricks. *Who has the most?* Let the children build the bricks into a tower and count them. *Who has fewer bricks than Kavita? Who has more bricks than Gareth?*

What is your number?
Hard

• *Discussing big numbers*
Number cards (1 to 50), number grid (1 to 100), Blu-tack, interlocking cubes
Shuffle the cards and give one to each child. In turn, let the children say their number and find it on the number grid. *Who has the biggest/smallest number?* That child attaches their number to the grid with Blu-tack and takes a cube. Repeat several times. *Who has the most cubes?*

Week 9

Coins to cards
Easy

• *Beginning to recognise numbers to 10*
Number cards (1 to 10), a ten-sided dice, 1p coins
Taking turns, the children roll the dice and count out that number of coins. They find the same number card and place the coins on the card. They continue until each of their cards has coins on it.

Bricks to cards
Medium

• *Beginning to recognise numbers to 10*
Number cards (1 to 10), small building bricks, plates
Give each child a set of number cards and ask them to put them in a line, face up, in order. Place a number of building bricks (up to 10) on a plate and let the children look at them. *Take a number card which you think matches the number of bricks on the plate.* Let one of the children count the bricks to check. Show the children the correct number card. *Who was correct?* Repeat several times.

Collecting coins

Hard

• *Beginning to recognise numbers to 10*
Number cards (1 to 10), 1p coins
Shuffle the cards and place them in a pile face down. The children play in pairs and take turns to take a card. They count out and keep the same number of coins. The first child to collect 20 or more coins is the winner.

Week 10

Flat or curved

Easy

• *Sorting 3-d shapes*
• *Matching similar 3-d shapes*
A selection of cubes, spheres and cones, a feely bag
Show the children the shapes and discuss which ones have flat or curved faces. Identify and discuss each shape as you put them in a bag. Retain one of each shape for the children to match. Pass the bag to a child and ask them to feel a shape. The child should describe the faces and try to remember the name of the shape. Ask the child to point to a matching shape and say something about it, e.g. *It is round all over.* Repeat.

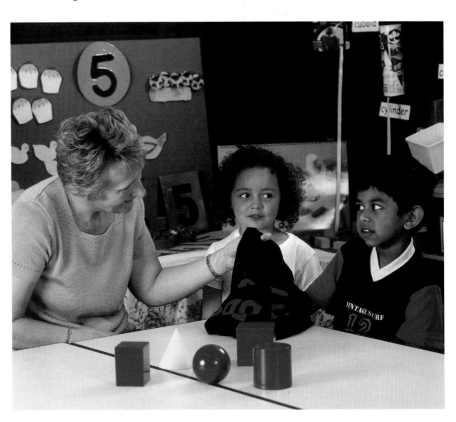

What was in the bag?

Medium

• *Sorting 3-d shapes*
Different-sized cubes and spheres, a feely bag
Show the children the shapes. Place one of each type on the table and the rest in the bag. Secretly remove one of the shapes from the bag and invite the children to question you to find out which shape has been removed. *Does it have flat sides? Is it curved?* When they think they have solved the mystery, let them reveal the shape. Were they correct? Repeat several times.

A colourful cube

Hard

• *Beginning to recognise cubes and spheres*
Nets of cubes, sticky tape
Give each child the net of a cube and ask them to decorate each face. Help them to fold along each edge and stick them together to make a box or cube. *How many faces did you have to decorate? What shape is each face?*

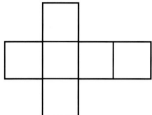

Week 11

Rows of coins

Easy

• *Recognising coins*
• *Ordering coins*
Real coins (1p, 2p, 5p, 10p, 20p, 50p, £1, £2), Blu-tack
Give each child a selection of coins and ask them to line them up in order of value, from the least to the most. The children secure their coins to the table with Blu tack to make a row of 1p coins, then 2p coins. Which coin do they have most of? Can they guess who has the most money?

Coin values

Medium

• *Recognising that £1 and £2 will buy lots*
Real and plastic coins (50p, £1, £2), long pieces of thin card, sticky tape
Show the children the real coins and discuss what they can buy with them. *Could you buy an outfit for teddy with this fifty pence? How many ice-creams can you buy with two pounds?* Fold the sheets of card to make zig-zag books and let the children stick an example of each plastic coin on separate pages. Next to each coin, the children can then draw an item that they could buy with that coin.

Money spinner

Hard

• *Recognising coins*
Real coins (£1, £2), interlocking cubes
Give each child ten cubes. The children take turns to choose to spin either the £1 or £2 coin. If they choose a £1 coin and it lands 'heads', they take a cube from the 'bank'. If it lands 'tails', they have to pay back a cube to the bank. If they spin a £2 coin, they either win or pay back two cubes. After several turns each, who has the most cubes?

Week 12

Daywear, nightwear

Easy

• *Recognising the difference between day and night*
Pictures of clothes, two large sheets of paper (one black, one white or blue), glue
Hang up the large sheets of paper and draw the moon on the black sheet and the sun on the white or blue sheet. Show the children the pictures of the clothes and discuss which ones they wear during the day and which at night. Let the children sort them into two sets and glue them to the large sheets of paper.

Weather chart
Medium

• *Recognising the concept of days separated by sleeps*
A weekly weather chart
Compile and display a weekly weather chart. Choose appropriate symbols for each type of weather. Discuss the current day's weather and put the symbols on the chart, as appropriate. Then do the same for the previous day's weather. When the chart is complete, ask the children about the weather on different days. *On which days this week did it rain? How many sleeps have you had since it was sunny?*

Favourite TV
Hard

• *Recognising the concept of days separated by sleeps*
Thin card, a paper fastener
Make a weekly chart of the children's favourite television programmes. Divide a circle into seven sections, labelling each section with a day of the week. Ask the children what they like to watch and write the names of their programmes in each section. Attach an arrow to the centre of the circle. Point the arrow at a programme on one of the days. *How many sleeps will you have before you can watch this programme again?*

Week 13

Number picture
Medium
Easy

• *Recognising numbers to 10*
Long sheets of paper divided and numbered into 10 segments
Give each child a sheet of paper and ask them to draw items that they like in the appropriate box. For example, they could draw three footballs in box 3, six hamburgers in box 6, ...

Matching toys
Medium

• *Estimating a number of objects and matching these to a numeral*
Sets of number cards (1 to 10), soft toys, a feely bag
Shuffle three or four sets of cards and give each child three cards to place face up in front of them. Place a few toys in the bag and pass it round for each child to feel and estimate the number of toys it contains. Tip the toys out of the bag and count them with the children's help. If a child has a number card matching the number of toys, they turn it over. Repeat several times. The first to turn over all three cards is the winner.

Counting track
Hard

• *Recognising numbers to 20*
Number tracks (1 to 20), a dice, counters, cubes
Give each child a number track and ask them to place a number of counters to match the number of each segment, e.g. nine counters in 9, seventeen counters in 17, ... Next, taking turns, the children roll the dice and move their cube that many sections along the track. As they land on each section, they clap or jump that many times. The children continue until they reach the end of the track.

Term 3

Week 1

Cube tracker
Easy

• *Using a number track*
Number track (1 to 10), cubes (in different colours)
The children take turns to choose, in secret, a number on the number track and clap that many times. The rest of the group counts the claps and says the number. If correct, the child who clapped puts a matching number of cubes in a tower on that number on the track. The children continue until each number has at least one cube tower on it. *Who has the most towers on the track?*

First to 20
Medium

• *Using a number track*
Number tracks (1 to 20), coins, counters
In pairs, the children place a counter on number 1 on the track. They toss the coin: heads move forwards three, tails move forwards two. Encourage the children to say which number they will land on and to count on from the previous number. If correct, the counter stays there, otherwise, they move it back one space. The winner is the first to 20. Repeat the game.

No more cards
Hard

• *Saying the next number*
Sets of number cards (1 to 10)
Deal out the cards so that each child has three. Place the last card face up on the table. The children take turns to place one of their cards on the table, but only if the next number has already been placed. They continue until one of them has placed all their cards.

Week 2

Counter grid
Easy

• *Counting up to 10 objects*
Different grids (1 x 3, 2 x 2, 1 x 5, 2 x 3, 2 x 5, 3 x 3, 4 x 2), counters
Give each group a grid of an appropriate size. Ask the children to put a small object, e.g. a counter, in each cell and count the total. Give them a different grid and ask them to repeat the exercise. Take one counter off the grid. *How many counters do you have now?* Can the children say the number without counting again?

Make a jigsaw
Medium

• *Counting to 20*
Jigsaws, thin card, scissors
Let the children choose a jigsaw, count the pieces in it and then put it together. Then encourage the children to make their own jigsaw by drawing a picture on card. Help them to cut it into up to 20 pieces. Can they remake their own jigsaw? Can they complete a friend's jigsaw?

Make a model
Hard

• *Counting to 20*
Number cards (1 to 10), building bricks
Shuffle the number cards and place them face down in a pile. The children take turns to take a card and say the number out loud. If they are correct, they take that number of building bricks. They continue until all the cards have been taken and then build a model with their bricks.

Week 3

Driving around
Easy

• *Beginning to use the language of direction*
Toy road layout or a large sheet of paper, toy cars
Use a road layout or draw one on a sheet of paper, making sure there are lots of turns. Give each child a toy car. The children take turns to give each other directions for driving their car and acting on another child's instructions. Encourage them to use the vocabulary 'forwards' and 'backwards'.

Backwards and forwards
Medium

• *Beginning to use the language of direction*
Small cards, soft toys
Make a set of direction cards, such as '3 steps forwards' and '2 steps backwards'. Shuffle the cards and place them face down in a pile. Give each child a soft toy. In turn, the children take one of the cards, hand it to you to read out the directions, and move their toy accordingly. Ask the child to replace the card and continue until each child has had several turns.

First to the edge
Hard

• *Beginning to use the language of direction*
Small cards, a number grid (1 to 100), different coloured counters
Make a set of direction cards, such as '3 squares forwards' and '2 squares backwards'. Shuffle the cards and place them face down in a pile. In turn, ask the children to place their counter in the middle of the grid (e.g. square 55), take a direction card and move their counter accordingly. They replace the card at the bottom of the pile. The first child to reach any edge of the grid is the winner.

Week 4

A sock hanger
Easy

• *Understanding that adding is increasing a set by a given number*
• *Increasing a set by one or two*
A wire coat hanger, clothes pegs, socks
Let each child peg a sock onto the coat hanger. *How many socks are on the hanger?* Invite a child to add another sock. *How many socks are on the hanger now?* Repeat several times, sometimes asking the children to add two more socks.

And one more is ...?
Medium

• *Counting on one or two*
Number cards (1 to 8), building bricks
Shuffle the cards and place them face down in a pile. In turn, the children take a card and take the same number of bricks. *How many bricks will you have if you take one more?* If the child answers correctly, they keep the bricks. Let the children have four turns each. *Who has the most bricks?*

Adding them up
Hard

• *Understanding that adding is increasing a set by a given number*
• *Counting on to find a total*
Number cards (1 to 10), a dice, building bricks
Shuffle the cards and place them face down in a pile. In turn, the children take a card and say the number. If correct, they take that number of bricks. They then roll the dice and take the appropriate number of bricks. They then combine their two sets of bricks. *How many bricks do you have in total?* Encourage the children to count on and say the whole calculation, rather than counting up from 1. *Seven and two make nine.* Repeat several times.

Week 5

Making a necklace
Easy

• *Adding by partitioning a set*
Beads (two colours), pieces of string, colouring pencils
Give each child six beads in two different colours and ask them to thread them onto a piece of string to make a necklace. *How many different patterns can you make with the same beads?* Let the children count the beads and make a record of the different patterns by drawing and colouring. Encourage the children to say the combinations. *Four and two make six. Three and three make six.*

Counter colours
Medium

• *Rearranging a set and partitioning in different ways*
Counters (red and blue)
Give each child some red and blue counters. Ask them to make a set of seven counters using both colours. They should make as many different sets as they can. Looking at each possible combination, ask the children to count the number of red and blue counters in each set and then say the calculation. *Three red counters and four blue counters make seven counters. Five red counters and two blue counters make seven counters.*

Sharing money
Hard

• *Adding by partitioning a set*
Two purses, 1p coins
Give the children two purses and seven coins and ask them to find out all the possible ways of sharing the coins between the two purses, e.g. *6p and 1p*.

Week 6

Taller or longer?
Easy

• *Comparing objects by size*
• *Distinguishing tall and long objects*
Let the children look around the classroom or the school to find items that can be described as 'tall'. Ask them to draw one of them. Repeat for long items. Display their work under two headings, 'tall' and 'long'. Encourage the children to describe their pictures using the words 'taller' and 'longer'.

How tall are we?
Medium

• *Comparing objects by size*
Three strips of paper (red, blue and yellow), Blu-tack
Attach the three strips of paper horizontally to the classroom door, red towards the top, blue in the middle and yellow further down. Let the children compare the heights. *Is anyone shorter than the yellow strip? Who is taller than the blue strip but shorter than the red strip? Who comes between two strips?* Help the children to write their names and position them at their actual heights on the door. Position your name and those of other adults at the appropriate heights.

 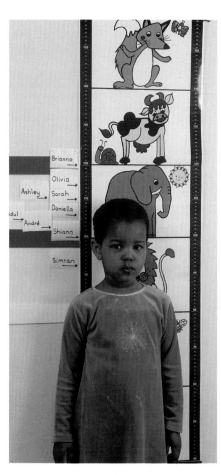

Land and sea

Hard

• *Comparing objects by size*
• *Distinguishing long and short objects*

Pictures of sea and land animals, large sheets of paper, glue

Show the children pictures of animals that live on the land and in the sea. Discuss whether each animal is long or short and sort them into two sets. Can they draw their own pictures of long and short animals? Sort them into two sets and stick them on separate sheets of paper, labelled 'long' and 'short'.

Week 7

Packing

Easy

• *Comparing full and empty for different containers*

Two different-sized suitcases, dressing-up clothes

Tell the children that you are taking the dressing-up clothes home to wash. Give them a small suitcase and ask if they can fold the clothes and place them in the case. As they fold the clothes, ask questions. *Is the case full yet? Is it half full? Do you think all the clothes will fit into the case? Why/why not? Oh dear! They don't fit. What shall we do?* Give the children a larger suitcase and repeat the process.

Mugfuls

Medium

• *Comparing full and empty for different containers*

Lentils, a jug, mugs, a tray

Over a tray, fill a jug with lentils. *How many mugs do you think we can fill with these lentils?* Discuss what is meant by a full mug. Let the children fill as many mugs as possible. *Is the jug empty yet? Did we guess right?*

Water bottles

Hard

• *Comparing full and empty for different containers*

A hot water bottle, a jug, water

Show the children the empty hot water bottle and ask them how many full jugs of water they think it holds. Make a note of their suggestions. Help a child to fill the jug with cold water and pour it into the hot water bottle. Repeat until the water bottle is full, encouraging the children to count. *How many jugs of water did it take to fill the water bottle? Did we guess right?* Screw in the top and let the children feel the weight of the full bottle. *Is the full bottle heavy or light?*

Week 8

Counting cubes

Easy

• *Comparing two quantities*
• *Discussing who has less and who has more*
Interlocking cubes
Each child counts out 20 cubes. They handle them to appreciate what that amount of cubes looks and feels like. They then take a new handful of cubes. *Who has the most?* Let the children build the cubes into a tower and count them. *Who has fewer bricks than Simran? Who has more bricks than Brian?*

Counters galore

Medium

• *Comparing two numbers*
Counters, squared paper
Each child takes a handful of counters and estimates how many they have. Give the children some squared paper and ask them to put their counters in a line, one per square. They then count their counters. *Who has made the shortest line? Who has the most counters?*

Big number, small number

Hard

• *Discussing big numbers*
Number cards (1 to 100), number grid (1 to 100), Blu-tack, 1p coins
Shuffle the cards and give one to each child. In turn, let the children say their number and find it on the number grid. *Who has the biggest/smallest number?* The holder attaches their number to the grid with Blu-tack and takes a 1p coin. Repeat several times. *Who has the most pennies?*

Week 9

From 10 to 1

Easy

• *Counting forwards and backwards to and from 10*
Number tracks (1 to 10), counters, coins
The children play in pairs. They each take a counter and place it on 10 on the number track. They take turns to spin the coin and move their counter backwards according to the fall of the coin: heads moves two spaces and tails moves one space. Encourage the children to say the number of each space that they land on. The first to reach number 1 is the winner.

Counting back

Medium

• *Counting forwards and backwards to and from 10*
Number cards (2 to 10), 1p coins
Shuffle the cards and place them face down in a pile. The children take turns to pick a card and count back from that number to 1. If they do it correctly, they take a coin. They replace the cards at the bottom of the pile. The first child to collect 20p wins.

End to end
Hard

- *Counting forwards and backwards to and from 20*
Number tracks (1 to 20), counters, coins
Each child places a counter on 10 on the number track. In turn, they spin a coin and move their counter accordingly: heads moves forwards two spaces, tails moves backwards two spaces. Encourage the children to say the number of the space they land on. The first child to reach either end of the track wins.

Week 10

Roll or slide?
Easy

- *Sorting 3-d shapes*
Dough or Plasticine, a ramp
Ask the children to make 3-d shapes with dough or Plasticine and to predict whether their shapes will roll or slide. Let them use the ramp to see if their predictions were correct. They then sort the shapes into categories: those that will roll and those that will slide. Ask them to make two new shapes – one that will roll and one that will slide. Can they make a shape that rolls and slides?

Feel the shape
Medium

- *Sorting 3-d shapes*
- *Beginning to discuss flat and curved faces*
3-d shapes, a feely bag, a ramp
Put one of the shapes in the bag and pass the bag to each child to feel. Ask them to say whether they think the shape will roll or slide. Make a note of their predictions. Take the shape out of the bag. *Does the shape have flat or curved faces?* Ask one of the children to place the shape on the ramp. *Is the shape rolling or sliding down the ramp? Did we guess right?* Repeat with the other shapes in the bag.

Making a cylinder
Hard

- *Beginning to discuss flat and curved faces*
Nets of cylinders drawn on thin card, sticky tape, a ramp
Cut out the nets of cylinders from card and give one to each child. Ask them to decorate what will be the outside of the cylinder. Help them to put the cylinder together. *If we want to roll the cylinder, which way up must it be? Which way must it be if we want it to slide?* Let the children test to see if their predictions were correct by sending their cylinders down the ramp.

Week 11

Coin tracks
Easy

• *Recognising coins*
• *Ordering coins*
Real coins (1p, 2p, 5p, 10p, 20p, 50p, £1, £2), Blu-tack
Give each child a set of coins and ask them to line them up in order of value, from the least to the most. The children take turns to choose a coin in secret. The others ask questions about the size, shape, colour and value to try to guess which coin the child has chosen.

What's it worth?
Medium

• *Recognising the relative values of pennies and pounds*
Real coins (1p, 2p, £1, £2), long pieces of thin card, sticky tape
Show the children the coins and discuss what they can buy with them. *Could you buy an ice-cream with this 2p? How many sweets can you buy with £1?* Fold the sheets of card to make zig-zag books and let the children stick an example of each coin on separate pages. Next to each coin, the children can then draw an item that they could buy with that coin.

Coin rubbings
Hard

• *Recognising coins*
Coins (1p, 2p, 5p, 10p, 20p, 50p, £1, £2), crayons
Let the children make a rubbing of each type of coin by placing a sheet of paper over one coin at a time and rubbing over it with the side of a crayon. Suggest that they use a different colour for each coin. *Which is your favourite shape for a coin? What can you buy with that coin?* Can the children name all the coins?

Week 12

Days of the week
Easy

• *Recognising that there are different days in the week*
A daily chart
With the children's help, put together a chart to show what they do on certain days of the week, from Monday to Friday. *George plays football on Tuesday. Zennija goes to her Gran's on Friday.* Discuss the fact that each week has the same days in it. *Which is your favourite day of the week?*

Different days
Medium

• *Recognising that there are different days in the week*
Two large sheets of paper, glue
Talk about the days of the week with the children and how people tend to do different things at the weekend. *Do we come to school at the weekend? What do you usually do on a Monday? What do you do at the weekend?* Ask the children to draw a picture of something that they do at the weekend and another to show what they do on a weekday. Separate the pictures into two sets and display them on the sheets of paper, headed 'weekdays' and 'weekends'.

**Weekday
or weekend?**

Hard

• *Distinguishing weekdays from weekends*
Card labels (Monday, Tuesday, ... Sunday)
Use sets of cards with the names of the days on them. Shuffle the
cards and place them face down in a pile. In turn, the children take a
card and place it in either a weekday or weekend pile. Help them to
read the name. When all the cards have been taken, say the names in
each set together. Ask the children to draw a picture illustrating their
favourite day. Display the pictures in two groups, 'weekdays' and
'weekend days'.

Week 13

Toy bag

Easy

• *Estimating small numbers of objects*
• *Counting to 20*
Number cards (1 to 20), about 20 small soft toys, a feely bag
Give each child three number cards and ask them to place them face
up in front of them. Secretly place several toys in the bag. Ask the
children to guess how many there are. Tip them out and count them
together. If one of the children has the correct number, they turn the
matching card over. The first child to turn over all three of their cards
is the winner.

Collecting cubes

Medium

• *Counting to 20*
Number tracks (1 to 20), counters, a coin, interlocking cubes
The children each place a counter on number 1 on the track and take
turns to spin a coin. They move along the track according to the fall
of the coin: heads move forwards two spaces, tails move forwards one
space. The children say the number of the space they move to and, if
correct, they collect that number of cubes. They continue until they
have all reached the end of the track. *Who has the most cubes?*

Around the grid

Hard

• *Counting to 20*
A large 4 x 5 grid, counters, a coin, interlocking cubes
Number each cell of the grid from 1 to 20 in order. Ask the children
to put their counters on number 1. In turn, the children spin the
coin and move according to how it falls: tails move sideways (in
either direction), heads move up or down. The children say the
number they land on and, if correct, they collect that number of
cubes. They continue until one of the children lands on number 20.
Who has the most cubes?

Counting

Counting to 10

Washing line necklaces

- *Counting to 6*
- *Matching numerals to sets of numbers*

Number cards (1 to 6), string, pegs, thread, beads

Hang up a length of string to make a washing line. Help the children to peg the number cards in order on the line. Thread the beads onto six lengths of thread: one bead on the first length, two beads on the second and so on. Let the children attach each set of threaded beads next to its matching number on the washing line.

Half a dozen eggs

- *Counting to 6*
- *Matching numerals to sets of numbers*

Half-dozen egg boxes, a dice, counters, number cards (1 to 6)

Ask each pair of children to place a number card in each section of the egg box. The children take turns to roll the dice, count the spots and pick up that number of counters to put in the matching section of the egg box. If the section has already been used, they miss a turn. The first pair to put the correct number of counters in all the sections wins.

Count the teddies

- *Counting to 10*

Several small teddy counters (or similar)

Ask pairs of children to take a handful of teddy counters. *Can you count your bears? Does anyone have six bears? Count them again to check.* Repeat with other numbers.

Apple trees

- *Counting to 10*

Paint, paintbrushes, adhesive circles

The children paint a tree and then attach ten circles to represent apples. When they have all finished, count the apples together. To extend this activity, let the children choose some red, green and yellow apples, but make sure there are still only ten apples on each tree.

Counting up to 10 objects

Egg boxes

- *Counting up to 6 objects*

Half-dozen egg boxes, interlocking cubes

Give each child an egg box. Ask the children to put one cube into each space. *How many cubes do you each have?* Ask the children to take out one cube. *How many do you have now?* Continue removing one cube each time. Repeat, adding cubes back into the egg box one at a time. Encourage the children to count their cubes each time.

Petals

• *Counting 6 objects*
Coloured paper, glue, scissors, green paint
Give each child a small paper circle to glue down to make the centre of a flower. Cut out six petals for each child and ask them to stick these around the flower centre. They then paint a stalk and leaves, count the flower petals and paint a number 6 next to the flower.

Rainbows

• *Counting 10 objects*
Paint, paintbrushes, old magazines, scissors, glue
Let the children paint a rainbow and then count the seven colours. Ask them to choose a number up to 10 and paint or stick that number of flowers, birds or animals cut from pictures in magazines onto their rainbow painting.

Finger-painted numbers

• *Counting 10 objects*
Long strips of paper, paint, paintbrushes, small adhesive stickers
Ask the children to paint the numbers 1 to 10 on their strip of paper. They then attach small stickers below each painted number to match. For example, they could put four circles below number 4, or six stars below number 6.

Counting to 20

Fingers and toes

• *Counting to 20*
Ask the children to take off their shoes and socks. Together, they count their toes up to 10 and continue with their fingers up to 20.

How many can I win?

• *Counting to 20*
A numbered dice (1 to 6), interlocking cubes, Post-it notes, a number line (1 to 20)
In groups of three, the children take turns to roll the dice and take that number of cubes. *Who can be the first to collect twenty cubes?* After each game, record on Post-it notes the children's names and their cube totals. Stick the notes on the number line. At the end of the session talk about the scores. *How many children collected twenty cubes? Which was the smallest number collected?*

Number grid

• *Counting to 20*
Large 4 x 5 grids, counters, interlocking cubes, coins
Number each cell of the grid from 1 to 20 in order. Divide the children into pairs and give each pair a grid. The children place their counters on a square near the middle. They take turns to spin a coin. If it lands heads, they move their counter across one space to the right or left. If it lands tails, they move it up or down one space. When they move, they say the number that they land on and take that number of cubes. The first to build a tower with 20 bricks is the winner.

Number snake

• *Counting to 20*
Chalk
Draw a number snake with 20 segments on the playground. Make each segment wide enough for three children to stand in it. Number each segment up to 20. Ask three children to jump along the snake as the rest of the children count up to 20.

Adding cubes

• *Counting to 20*
Number cards (1 to 20), interlocking cubes, sultanas
The children play in pairs. Give each child a number card. Each pair counts the same number of cubes as shown by the numbers on both cards to find the total of their two cards. How many cubes does each pair have? The pair with the highest/lowest total wins a sultana. Repeat several times.

Counting to and from 10

Sand rocket

- *Counting forwards and backwards to and from 10*
- *Recognising numbers to 10*

A sand tray, interlocking cubes or cylinders

Let the children make a rocket using interlocking cubes or cylinders. Make a number line from 1 to 10 in the sand. Together, count down the number line from 10 to 1 and then let the children launch their rockets, shouting 'Blast off!' after 1.

Count down

- *Counting forwards and backwards to and from 10*

Number cards (1 to 10)

Give each child a set of number cards. Ask them to make a number line with them. Invite a child to call out a number. All the children count down from that number, shouting 'Blast off!' at the end of the count. Extend the children using number cards to 20, if appropriate.

Number the track

- *Counting forwards and backwards to and from 10*

Number cards (1 to 10), red and blue counters, cubes (labelled 1, 2, 3 in blue and 1, 2, 3 in red)

Give each pair of children a set of number cards to make a number track. The children place their counters in the middle of the track, i.e. on 5. Those who have a red counter move backwards and those who have a blue counter move forwards. The children take turns to roll the cube and move one of the counters according to the roll if it matches their colour. The winner is the first to reach the end of the track. Extend the children using number cards to 20 and counters starting at 10, if appropriate.

Recognising numerals

A table for 4

- *Recognising the numeral 4*
- *Counting up to 4*

A table, card labels ('4', 'four')

In a corner of the room, set out a table with the labels '4' and 'four' on it. Encourage the children to find objects in the room which have associations with 4, e.g. a car with four wheels, a toy dog with four legs, four building bricks joined together, a picture with four flowers, a birthday card for a fourth birthday. Let the children place the items on the '4' table.

How many in the box?

- *Recognising numbers to 6*

Number cards (1 to 6), soft toys, a box, a number track (1 to 6)

Give each child a set of number cards and ask them to order the cards, using the number track as a model. Without saying the numbers, drop into the box up to six toys, one at a time. *How many toys are in the box? Who can find that number? Who can count the toys out of the box for us to check?* Repeat several times.

Dice numbers

- *Recognising numbers to 6*

Number cards (1 to 6), a large dice

Give each child a set of number cards and ask them to place them in order. Roll a large dice. The children turn over the card that matches the dice number. Repeat until all the cards have been turned over.

Cymbal crashes

- *Recognising numbers 1 to 10*
- *Counting sounds*

Cymbals, interlocking cubes

Crash the cymbals together five times, asking the children to count each crash. *How many crashes were there?* If necessary repeat and count together. The children then collect five cubes each. Count them together. When the children are able to count the crashes of the cymbals easily, try turning your back on them and repeat the activity. The children will need to listen harder as they cannot see the count.

Bang the drum

• *Recognising numbers to 6*
• *Counting sounds*
Number cards (1 to 6), a number track (1 to 6), a drum, a beater
Give each child a set of number cards. Ask the children to put the cards in order. Show them the number track, if necessary. Tap out four beats on the drum. *How many beats have I tapped? Can you find the card with a four? Is everyone holding up the four?* Point to the number on the number track. Repeat with different numbers. Extend the activity by turning your back so the children cannot see the drum being tapped.

Missing numbers

• *Beginning to recognise numbers to 10*
Number cards (1 to 10)
Ask the children lay out the number cards in order. Ask them to close their eyes while you turn over a card. When they open their eyes, encourage them to identify the missing number. *How do you know?* Extend the activity by turning over two numbers. *Is the number track right? What is wrong with it? Can you tell me how to make it right?*

Domino train

• *Matching numbers*
A set of dominoes
Ask the children to make a train of dominoes whose adjoining carriages (individual dominoes) have a matching number of dots. How long a train of dominoes can they make?

Run around

• *Recognising numbers to 10*
Pieces of carpet or felt (with numbers 1 to 20 written on)
In a spacious area, ask the children to lay out the numbers. The children place the pieces of carpet on the floor at random. Call out instructions, e.g. *One more than six* or *One less than fourteen*. The children must run and stand on or by that number. Who gets to the correct number first each time?

Where is teddy sitting?

• *Recognising numbers to 12*
Number cards (1 to 12), a teddy bear
Lay out the number cards 1 to 12 to form a number track. Count together along the number track. Place a teddy bear next to individual numbers. *What number is teddy sitting by? How can we find out if Rosie is right?* Count along the number line until you reach the number with the teddy on it. Repeat several times.

Can you feel the number?

• *Recognising numbers to 6*
A number track (1 to 6)
Invite a child to stand with their back facing the rest of the children. Use your finger to trace a number up to 6 on the child's back. *Which number have I traced? Can you find it on the number track?* Extend the activity by asking the children to draw the number that you have traced on a sheet of paper or on the carpet using a finger.

Do as we say!

• *Recognising numbers to 20*
Numerals (1 to 20)
Lay out the numerals to 20 in a long line. Choose a child and ask the other children to give them instructions. The child runs to the numeral and does the action. *Number six, hop six times. Number eight, count up to eight. Number fifteen, say the number that comes next. Number ten, say the number that comes before that number.* Repeat with different children following the instructions.

Jumping along to 10

• Recognising numbers 1 to 10
• Counting to 10
Pieces of carpet or felt (with numbers 1 to 10 written on), small number cards (1 to 10)
Give the children the pieces of carpet or felt. Help them to lay them in numerical order to make a track across the floor or playground. The children then take turns to pick up a small number card. They jump along the track until they reach the number on their card. Encourage all of the children to join in with the counting and remembering when to stop. The whole group could jump the correct number of jumps on the spot.

Representing numerals

Tower blocks

• Writing numbers 1 to 10
• Counting sets of numbers to 10
Number cards (1 to 10), small bricks or interlocking cubes
The children arrange the number cards in a line, in order from 1 to 10. They copy each number in turn onto a piece of paper, then build a tower of bricks or cubes to match.

Dough numbers

• Modelling numbers to 9
Number cards (1 to 9), dough, peg board pegs
Give each child a number card, as appropriate. Ask them to make a dough number to match the number on their card. They collect and stick the matching number of pegs in the dough number. Can they group themselves according to their numbers and in the correct order?

Sandy numbers

• Drawing numbers to 9
• Counting up to 9 objects
A sand tray
Mark out a number track in the sand. Let the children write the numerals 1 to 9 (or a lower number, if appropriate) along the track using their fingers. Ask them to place a matching number of objects next to each number on the track, e.g. two buckets, four spades.

Comparing and ordering numbers

More and less

Numbers in a row

• *Talking about big and small numbers*
Pieces of carpet or felt (with numbers 1 to 10 written on)
Arrange the numbers 1 to 10 in a line. Count together along the number line. Ask a child to sit behind each of the numbers. *Who is sitting behind the biggest number? Who is sitting behind the smallest number? How do you know?* If the children find this easy, ask the ten children to pick up their number and let them stand in any order. *Who is holding the biggest number now? How do you know it is still William?*

How many claps?

• *Comparing two quantities*
Number cards (1 to 10)
Ask a child to clap seven times. *How many times did Evie clap? Which number card shall we give Evie?* Ask another child to clap eight times. *Which card shall we give Andrew? Ella, can you clap fewer times than Evie? How many claps shall we ask Ella to make? Who clapped the most times? How do we know? How do we know that eight is more than seven and three?*

Numbered jumpers

• *Discussing more and less*
Number cards (1 to 10), Blu-tack
Ask two children each to choose a number card. Attach the cards to their jumpers with Blu-tack. In turn, ask the children to raise fingers to match the numbers on the jumpers. *Who has the biggest/smallest number?* Check by counting the number of fingers raised.

Colourful flowers

• Discussing more and less
Number cards (1 to 10), paint, paintbrushes
Ask the children to paint a colourful picture of some flowers. When they have finished, ask them to count the number of different colours they have used in their painting. Then invite the children to choose the matching number card. *How many colours have you used, Alice? Can you find the matching number card? Who has used the most/fewest colours? How do you know?*

Waiting in line

• Comparing two numbers
Two sets of number cards (1 to 10)
Give eight children number cards 1 to 8 and ask them to stand in a line. Give four children number cards 1 to 4 and ask them to stand in line next to the first line. *Which line is the longer/shorter? How do you know?* Ask the children with the numbers 1 to 4 to make matching number pairs. *How many children are without a partner?* Repeat with different sets of cards.

Win a sultana

• Comparing two numbers
Number cards (1 to 20), a packet of sultanas
The children play in pairs. Each child takes a number card. *Can you read both your numbers? Who has the larger number? Does everyone agree?* The child in each pair with the larger number wins a sultana. Let the children choose different cards and repeat the questioning. Vary the activity by letting the winner be the child with the smaller number.

Ordering numbers

Brick towers

• *Ordering numbers to 10*
Bricks, sets of small sticky labels (numbered 1 to 10)
Ask the children, in pairs, to make towers, ten bricks tall. Together, count the bricks in each tower. Give each pair a set of sticky labels to number the bricks. Ask the children to knock down the towers. Which pair is the first to make a correctly numbered tower or line of bricks?

Stack the boxes

• *Ordering numbers to 6*
Stacking boxes and trays, sticky labels
Label the stacking boxes and trays to indicate their contents. Give them a number to help the children put them in order. *What do we keep in box four? Which box do we stack on top of box number four?*

Getting into line

• *Ordering numbers to 6*
Large number cards (1 to 6)
Place the number cards face down in any order on the floor. Choose six children to pick up a card and ask the rest of the group to put them in number order. *Who is holding number four? What number is Harriet holding?*

Front door numbers

• *Talking about big and small numbers*
Number grid (1 to 100)
The children draw their home and write in their front door number (or ask them to make one up). Can they say the number and find it on the number grid? Display the houses in number order, from smallest to biggest, and say the numbers. *Who lives in the house with the biggest/smallest number?*

Adding

Counting on

Race to 20

• Counting on and back from a given number

Pieces of carpet or felt (with numbers 1 to 20 written on), a coin

Lay the pieces of carpet in order to form a number track. Two children stand on number 1. Two other children take turns to toss the coin: heads move forwards one, tails move forwards two. They choose one of the children on the track and move them according to the toss of the coin. *Jon is on fourteen. The coin has landed on heads. Which number must Jon move onto?* Encourage the children to jump and count the one or two steps forward, until they reach 20. Extend the game by starting at 20 and counting back.

Where will teddy land?

• Counting on from a given number

Pieces of carpet or felt (with numbers 1 to 20 written on), a coin, soft toys

Lay out the pieces of carpet to form a number track and ask three children to place soft toys on different numbers up to 10. Check that the children can identify the numbers. They may need to count from 1. The children take turns to toss a coin for their toys: heads move forwards two, tails move backwards one. They work out and say where the toys on the track will move to. The child whose toy reaches 20 first wins.

A tin of marbles

• Counting on one or two to find a total

Marbles, a tin, a number track (1 to 10), Post-it notes

Drop six marbles into the tin one at a time and ask the children to raise a finger each time they hear a marble dropping. *Can you show me with your fingers how many marbles there are in the tin? Who can put a Post-it note on number six on the number track?* Count on from 1 along the number track to show that the number is correct. *How many marbles will there be if I put two more in the tin?* Show the two extra marbles but do not drop them into the tin yet. Practise counting on by putting your hand on the tin and saying *Six*, then count on, *Seven, eight* as you point to the two extra marbles. Repeat for different numbers.

Shy bears

• Understanding that adding is increasing a set by one or two

A number track (1 to 10), a cloth, at least ten teddy bears, Post-it notes

Count out four teddy bears in unison. Place the cloth over the teddies. *How many teddies are there? Who can put a Post-it note on number four on the number track? If I put two more teddies under the cloth, how many will there be?* Place two teddies near the cloth. Check by counting on, putting your hand on the cloth and saying, *Four*, then touch the two teddies saying, *Five, six*. Reinforce this by pointing to the Post-it note on the number track. *Count on two: five, six*. Repeat for different numbers.

Cube totals

• Understanding that adding is increasing a set by one or two

Numerals (1 to 10), interlocking cubes

Hold up number 5. Working in pairs, one child takes five cubes. Hold up number 2. The second child takes two cubes. *How many cubes are there altogether?* Encourage the children to count on from 5. *Five and two more make seven*. Repeat with different numbers.

One or two more than

• Increasing and decreasing a set by one or two
Small sticky labels
Write the numbers 1 to 5 on separate sticky labels. Give a set to each child and ask them to stick the numbers to their fingers in order. Show them the correct order on your hand. Ask the children to fold down their numbered fingers into a fist. *Can you show me three fingers? Can you count them with me? How many fingers will be standing when we hold up two more fingers? Three and two make five. How many will be standing when we fold down two? We are back to three again.* Repeat for similar examples.

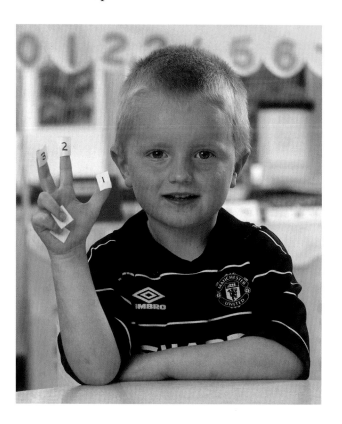

• Increasing and decreasing a set by one or two
A long sheet of paper, ten soft toys
Divide and number the paper into ten segments. Leave enough space for a soft toy to fit on each segment without obscuring the numbers. Ask the children to put three toys on the first three segments of the track. *How many teddies are there on the track? How many will there be if you put two more on the track? Five. Three and two make five.* Continue adding and taking away the toys, saying the calculations.

• Increasing a set by one or two
A tin box, small pebbles, number cards (1 to 10)
Ask the children to make a number track with their cards. As you drop the pebbles in the tin, ask the children to point to each number. *How many pebbles are in the tin? Can you all point to the number on your number track? Listen while I drop in two more. How many pebbles will there be in the tin now?*

ADDING

Tea party

• *Adding one more to a small set*
Home corner items, several dolls
Ask the children to set the table for three dolls. *How many chairs do you need for the dolls? How many cups do you need?* Give the children time to set the table, then show another doll. *Can this doll come to tea too? How many more chairs will you need? How many chairs will you have altogether?*

One more toy

• *Adding one more to a small set*
Several soft toys, a box
Ask the children to count out three toys. *Can you count the toys as Jack puts them into the box? How many toys did Jack put in the box? Ellie, can you put one more toy in the box? How many toys are there now? Alex, can you count them to check that we have four?* Continue adding one more toy and asking similar questions.

How many beads?

• *Adding one more to a small set*
Pieces of string knotted at one end, large beads
Give each child a piece of string and ask them to thread three or four beads onto it. Ask the children to touch each bead as you count together. *How many beads will you have if you thread on one more?* Ask the children to thread on another bead to check. Repeat several times.

Jumping jacks

• *Adding one more to a small set*
• *Recognising numbers up to 10*
A large number track (1 to 10)
Lay the number track on the floor. Choose one or more children to move along it. *Can you jump along the track until you get to number four?* Count with the children as they jump. *What number are you standing on? How many jumps have you made to get to four? If you jump one more space, where will you land?* Let the children check by jumping one more to see if they are correct. *One more than four is five.*
Continue counting on one more until they reach the end of the track.

Birthday candles

• *Adding one more to a small set*
Cake candles and holders, a birthday cake, matches
Choose a child who has a birthday the following day. *How old are you today, Alice? Can you put that number of candles on your cake? Ben, how old will Alice be tomorrow? Do we have the right number of candles on her cake? What will we need to do to make the number of candles correct for tomorrow?* Let the birthday girl/boy add another candle to the cake and check the total number. Light the candles and ask the child to blow them out.

Finding totals

Hi five!

• *Rearranging a set and partitioning in different ways*
Number cards (0 to 5), interlocking cubes
Give six children number cards 0 to 5. Ask them to make a tower of cubes to match the number on the card. The cubes should all be the same colour. *Jake, how many cubes did you count out to match your number? Four. Who must sit by Jake so that together you have five cubes? Dharma. Why? Because she has one cube.* Encourage each pair of children to say their calculation.

Money boxes

• *Adding by partitioning a set*
Number cards (1 to 10), 1p coins, cards with money boxes drawn on them
Give each pair of children some 1p coins and two money box cards. Choose a number card. The children read the number and take that number of coins. They place some of the coins on each money box card. Ask them to read the amount in each box as a calculation. *Four and three make seven. Six and one make seven.* How many different sets can they make with the same number? Repeat with different numbers.

Sheep in the field

• *Rearranging a set and partitioning in different ways*

Toy sheep or pictures of sheep drawn by children, a sheet of green paper divided by a painted hedge

Count out six sheep. Ask the children to put all the sheep in one of the fields. *Mark, can you put one of the sheep in the other field? How many sheep are left in the first field? Let's say the sum together. Five and one make six.* Let the children continue moving the sheep one at a time. Ask the children to say each sum as the sheep are moved.

Cube combinations

• *Adding by partitioning a set*

Interlocking cubes (in two colours)

Working in pairs, the children take 10 cubes in two colours. They make two cube towers, one in each colour. Can the children say a number sentence for the towers they have made? *How many different towers can we make with this number of cubes?*

Money

Recognising coins

Coin colours

• *Recognising coins*
Real coins (1p, 2p, 5p, 10p)
Place the coins on a sheet of paper. *Which are the bronze/brown coins? Who can find a bronze coin? Who can find a different bronze coin? How is it different?* Ask each child to take a bronze coin and to look for a number on it. *If your coin has a '1' on it, can you hold it up?* Repeat with the 2p coin. Repeat the activity with the silver coins.

A coin for everyone

• *Recognising coins*
• *Recognising that £1 and £2 will buy more than pennies*
A selection of real coins
Place a selection of real coins on the floor. Ask the children to find a particular coin. *Hannah, can you find a ten pence coin?* Differentiate by shape or colour. *Alex, can you find a coin that is not round?* When each child has chosen a coin, ask about the relative values. *Which coin do you think is best for buying lots of ice-creams? Why?*

Rolling for coins

• *Recognising coins*
**A cube (labelled '1p', '2p', '5p', '10p', '£1', '£2'),
coins (1p, 2p, 5p, 10p, £1, £2)**
The children take turns to roll the cube and pick up the matching coin. At the end of the game, the child with the most £2 coins is the winner. Vary the game by choosing the child with the fewest 1p coins as the winner.

Ordering coins

Put them in order

• *Recognising the relative value of coins*
Coins (1p, 2p, 5p, 10p)
Give each child a coin. Hold up a 1p coin. *Who has a coin like this one?* Invite those children to stand in a line. Repeat with the 2p, 5p and 10p coins until all the coins are lined up in order. Total the value of the complete line as the children, in turn, say the value of their coin. Ask who is holding a coin that is worth the most or that you can buy the most with. Repeat for the coin of the least value.

Using coins

What can you buy?

• *Recognising that we use coins for buying and selling*
1p coins, saucers, classroom objects priced up to 6p
Give each pair of children a saucer of 1p coins. Then ask the children to read the prices of different items with you. *Teddy costs four pence. Can you count out four pence to buy the teddy?* Let them replace their coins and repeat with other objects.

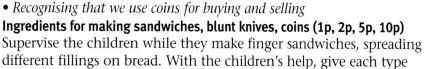

Finger sandwiches

• *Recognising that we use coins for buying and selling*
Ingredients for making sandwiches, blunt knives, coins (1p, 2p, 5p, 10p)
Supervise the children while they make finger sandwiches, spreading different fillings on bread. With the children's help, give each type of sandwich a different price. Let the children use the coins to buy the sandwiches.

Bring-and-buy sale

• *Recognising that we use coins for buying and selling*
Items to sell, card labels
Involve parents in a fund-raising bring-and-buy sale. (It is probably better to hold it at the end of a session.) Ask the children to bring in a small item which someone else might like to buy. Let the children help with pricing the items and ask them to set them out on a table. When the parents arrive, encourage them to let the children find the correct coins to buy the items.

Pounds

• *Recognising that £1 and £2 will buy a lot*
Coins (£1, £2), objects priced at £1 or £2, a hand puppet
Tell the children that the puppet has some money and wants to buy something. *The puppet wants to buy the book. Which coin will he need to use? The two pound coin. Can he pay any other way?* Explain that two £1 coins are equivalent to a £2 coin.

What can I afford?

• *Recognising that £1 and £2 will buy a lot*
Shop or café items (e.g. sandwiches, cakes, ...) priced with a single coin value (i.e 5p not 7p or 8p), real coins (all denominations)
Set up the role play area as a café or shop. Let the children take turns to be a shopkeeper or waiter/waitress and a customer. The customer chooses a coin and tells the shopkeeper what they want to buy. *A bun costing two pence please.* The shopkeeper checks the coin. *Have you got a two pence coin?* If the customer reveals a different coin, the shopkeeper asks what the customer would like to buy instead for that price. Repeat several times.

First come, first served

• *Recognising that £1 and £2 will buy a lot but 1p coins very little*
Coins (all denominations), priced classroom objects
Hold up a book priced £1 and ask the children to find the correct coin to buy the book. The first child to do so correctly wins the book. Repeat with the other priced objects.

Choose a coin

• *Recognising that £1 and £2 will buy a lot but 1p coins very little*
Two plates with different types of biscuits priced 1p and 2p, books priced £1 and £2, a feely bag, coins (1p, 2p, £1, £2)
Choose one child to be the shopkeeper. Put the coins in a feely bag. Taking turns, the children try to identify a coin they can feel in the bag. They withdraw the coin to see if they are correct. They then go to the shop and give the shopkeeper the correct coin to buy one of the biscuits or one of the books.

Measures

Length

Long socks/ short socks

• *Comparing length*

A supply of long and short socks, a skipping rope or a long ribbon

Divide the room into two with the rope or ribbon. Explain that all the children wearing or holding long socks should sit on one side of the ribbon and those with short socks on the other side. Are the children able to sort themselves into groups with either long or short socks? *How did you know if the socks were long or short?* You may need to explain that long socks come up to the knees but short socks just cover the ankle.

Tall tower

• *Comparing height*

Several bricks

Ask a child to build a brick tower. Ask another child to build a tower that is shorter than the first one. *Is Joe's tower shorter than Jessie's tower? How do you know? Who has built the taller/shorter tower?* Repeat with different children building towers.

Snakes alive!

• *Comparing length*

Dough or Plasticine

With the dough or Plasticine, ask each child to make a long snake and a short snake. *Can you point to your long snake? Which is the shorter snake? How do you know which is longer and which is shorter?*

Big potato, small potato

• *Comparing objects by size*

Different-sized potatoes, a feely bag

Show the children two different-sized potatoes and ask them which is smaller and which is larger. Place the potatoes in the bag. Ask a child to feel inside and take out the larger potato. Look at the other potato to check if the child is correct. Place both back in the bag and ask another child to take out the smaller potato. If the children find this easy, include a medium-sized potato as well and ask similar questions.

Pencils

• *Comparing objects by size*
• *Distinguishing long and short objects*

Two pencils of very different lengths

Show the children the two pencils. *Are these pencils the same length?* (You may wish to stand the pencils on the table so that the difference is apparent.) Encourage the children to use the words 'longer' and 'shorter' rather than 'big' and 'little'. *Which pencil is the longer pencil? How do you know?* Repeat with other objects.

Beds for bears

- *Comparing objects by size*
- *Distinguishing long and short objects*

Three bears (one long, one medium-sized, one short), cardboard boxes or wooden bricks or soft toys

Ask the children to choose suitably-sized boxes to make beds for the bears, or to make pretend beds using wooden bricks. *Which bear is sleeping in the longest bed? How do you know he is the longest bear? Is he the tallest bear too?*

Tall tower, long wall

- *Comparing objects by size*
- *Distinguishing tall and long objects*

Construction toys

Using construction toys, ask the children to make a long wall with tall towers at either end. *Who has made the longest wall? Who has made the tallest tower?*

Taller or wider

• *Distinguishing between tall and long objects*
• *Distinguishing between wide and narrow objects*
Ask a child to stand by a table. *Which is taller, the table or Justin? How do you know?* Ask another child to lie down alongside the table. *Which is wider, the table or Heidi?* Can the children find anything narrower than the table? (A child who will fit between the two table legs.) If the table is oblong in shape, it will allow for some interesting discussion on length and width.

Weight

Sand buckets

• *Comparing objects by weight*
Sand, a scoop, two small similar-sized buckets
Let the children fill one bucket with sand. Ask a child to pick up one bucket in each hand. *Which bucket is heavier? How do you know?* Let the children pour the sand into the empty bucket. *Which is the heavier bucket now?*

Bags of potatoes

• *Comparing objects by weight*
Potatoes, two identical-sized bags
Without the children seeing, place two potatoes in one of the bags. Ask a child to pick up the empty bag and the one with two potatoes in. *Which bag is heavier? Which is lighter?* Pass the bags around. *Does everyone agree?* Reveal the contents and ask the children to explain why one bag was heavier than the other. Show the children the bag containing the potatoes. Ask them how they can make the lighter bag heavier. Ask volunteers to pick up the bags to see if it has worked.

MEASURES

Corn flakes or rice?

• *Comparing objects by weight*
Two small similar-sized buckets, corn flakes, rice
Ask the children to fill one of the buckets with the corn flakes and the other with rice. Before lifting the buckets to test for weight, ask the children which bucket they think will be lighter/heavier. Pass the buckets around and ask each child to tell you which they think is the heavier/lighter bucket.

Bathroom scales

• *Comparing weight*
Bathroom scales, a large teddy bear
Ask a child to stand on the scales and read the measurement (treat this activity with sensitivity). *How many kilos does Amy weigh?* Let other children try before weighing a large teddy bear. *How heavy is teddy? Does he weigh more or less than Amy? How do we know?*

Heavy and light objects

• *Comparing objects by weight*
Heavy items (a can of beans, a bag of sugar, ...), light items (a feather, a pair of socks, ...), two carrier bags, two rings or hoops, two labels ('heavier than the sugar' and 'lighter than the sugar')
Place the hoops on the floor and lay a label next to each of them. Put the sugar into one of the carrier bags. Ask the children, in turn, to lift the bag. *Can you see anything that is heavier than the sugar? Can you pick it up to see if it feels heavier than the bag of sugar?* Put a lighter item into the other carrier bag. Let the children, in turn, lift both bags, one in each hand. *Is this bag heavier than the one with the sugar in it? What do you think, Safa? Which hoop shall we put the pair of socks in?* Repeat with the other objects.

Wet sand, dry sand

• *Comparing objects by weight*
Two identical-sized buckets, sand, water
Fill one bucket with dry sand and one with wet sand. Ask the children to lift both buckets, one in each hand. *What do you notice about the buckets? Which is heavier? Which is lighter?*

Bags of apples

• *Comparing objects by weight*
Two identical bags or buckets, apples
Empty most of the apples into one of the bags or buckets and ask a child to lift the bags, one in each hand. *Which is the heavier/lighter bag? Can you make the heavier bag lighter? What will you need to do?* Also ask how the lighter bag could be made heavier.

A balancing act

• *Comparing objects by weight*
A bucket balance, two toys or shoes of different weights
Ask a child to place one of the toys or shoes in the bucket balance. *What has happened to the bucket? Why has it gone down? What do we need to do to make the buckets balance?* Ask the children to find different objects to put on the balance to compare their weights.

Capacity

Biscuit barrel

• *Comparing full and empty for different containers*
A packet of biscuits, an empty tin, a teddy bear
Tell the children that the teddy bear is sad as there are no biscuits left in the tin. *How do we know the tin is empty? Who would like to put some biscuits into the tin?* Count together as one of the children puts the biscuits in the tin. *Is the tin empty or full now? Can I turn the tin upside down? Why/why not? When could I turn it upside down?*

Pasta fill

• *Comparing full and empty for different containers*
Two different-sized containers, a packet of pasta shapes, a tray
Show the children the containers and ask them which holds more. *How can we find out? Who would like to fill the taller container with pasta?* Let one of the children fill the taller container over the tray. *Is the container full? How do you know? What do you think will happen if we pour the full container into the empty one?* Ask one of the children to try. *Will we get all the pasta in? Why not? Which container holds more?*

Which holds more?

• *Comparing capacity*
One large and one small container, water, sand, rice, small pasta shapes
Hold up both containers and ask the children which they think will hold more water. Ask them to explain why they think the larger container will hold more. Fill the large container with water and ask the children to predict what might happen if the water is poured into the small container. Let a child try it out. Reverse the procedure, asking a child to fill the smaller container with water and asking what will happen when the water is poured into the larger container. Repeat the activity, encouraging the children to use sand, rice and pasta shapes to compare how much each container holds.

Time

Bear's bedtime

• *Talking about day and night*
• *Recognising the difference between day and night*
Pyjamas, daytime clothes, a large teddy bear
Dress the teddy bear in pyjamas. *When do we wear our pyjamas?* Discuss bedtime, night-time and going to sleep. Now dress teddy in some daytime clothes. *What do we do during the day? How is daytime different from night-time?*

Sun and moon

• *Talking about day and night*
• *Recognising the difference between day and night*
Two large cloths or sheets of paper (one black, one white or blue), a sparkly sun, moon and stars, safety pins or Velcro, old magazines, scissors
Display the cloths or paper sheets next to each other, explaining that one (black) represents night-time and the other (white or blue) represents daytime. Hold up a big sparkly sun. *Shall we pin this onto the day sky or night sky? When do we see the sun? What shall we pin onto the night sky?* Do the same with the moon and stars. *Are there any animals or birds that prefer coming out at night?* Let the children look for pictures of them in old magazines. Help them to cut them out and stick them to the night sky picture.

Bedtime drinks

• *Talking about day and night*
• *Recognising the difference between day and night*
Milk, a saucepan, drinking chocolate, a whisk, mugs
Discuss drinks that we drink at different times of the day. Ask the children to make suggestions for drinks for breakfast and bedtime. *Claire, what do you like to drink before you go to bed? Does it help you sleep?* Heat some milk in a saucepan, add the drinking chocolate and whisk up the mixture. Pour it into mugs and let the children enjoy a frothy bedtime drink.

Teddy bears' picnic

- *Recognising the concept of days separated by sleeps*
Card, teddy bears, toys for a tea party
Tell the children there is a teddy bears' picnic in four days' (sleeps')
time. Write the name of the four days before the picnic on separate
pieces of card and pin them up. Count the four days together. As the
picnic approaches, remove each day. *How many more sleeps until the
picnic?* On the day allow the children to play with the toys to act out
the teddy bears' picnic.

Birthdays

- *Recognising the concept of days separated by sleeps*
A calendar, pictures or photographs of the children
Mark the children's birthdays on the calendar. Pin up pictures or
photographs of children who have a birthday during a particular
month. On a daily basis, cross out each day on the calendar and
count how many sleeps there will be before one of their birthdays.

Swimming day

- *Recognising the concept of days separated by sleeps*
Write down the days of the week and ask the children to think of
something significant that happens on those days. *What happens on a
Wednesday? Swimming. Today is Monday.* Point to Monday. *How many
sleeps until your swimming day?* Repeat with other days.

Teddy's weekend

- *Distinguishing weekdays from weekends*
Paper
Fold pieces of paper in half and label the halves 'Saturday' and
'Sunday'. Give each child a labelled piece of paper and ask them to
draw pictures to show what teddy could be doing while he is away at
the seaside at the weekend.

Jump today

- *Recognising that there are different days in the week*
A calendar
Look at the class calendar and work out what day it is, e.g. Tuesday.
Together, the children chant the days of the week and jump up when
they get to Tuesday.

Monday's child

- *Recognising that there are different days in the week*
Recite the poem 'Monday's child' to the children. Make a large copy
of the poem and display it. Ask the children to find out the day on
which they were born and to draw a picture to match that part of the
verse. Display the pictures next to the poem. Group the children
according to the day they were born on and teach them the relevant
part of the poem.

Day cars

- *Recognising that there are different days in the week*
Small Post-it notes, seven toy cars
Write the days of the week on the Post-it notes and stick them to the
cars. Keeping the days in order, give one car to seven children and
ask each one to make up a story of a journey for their car. *It's Monday
and we're off in our red car to the supermarket.*

Shape and space

2-d shape

Which window?

• *Matching similar 2-d shapes*
• *Recognising squares and circles*
Three pictures of different scenes, pictures of objects/animals, Blu-tack
Draw three windows on a flip chart or the board: one circular, one square and one triangular. Point to the round window. *What shape is this window? Yes, it is round. We call it a circle.* Repeat with the other windows. Stick a picture in each of the windows. *What can you see through the square window? A fire station. I can see a giraffe – which window am I looking through?*

Shape search

• *Matching similar 2-d shapes*
• *Recognising squares and circles*
Four equal length sticks, a hoop, classroom objects, labels ('square', 'circle')
Hold up the hoop and ask the children what shape it is. Most children will say that it is round. *The shape is round but we call it a circle.* Show the children the 'circle' label and explain that this is the word for circle. Show the children the four sticks and point out that each one is the same length. Use the sticks to make a square shape. Repeat the questioning and show the children the 'square' label. Ask them to find objects in the room that match both shapes and place them in the square or circle as appropriate.

Wood block prints

• *Recognising squares and circles*
A piece of sponge soaked in thick paint, paper, wood block circles and squares
Discuss the shapes on the wood blocks. Show the children how to make prints by dipping a wood block into the paint on the sponge, then pressing it down on the paper. Encourage the children to print rather than paint with the blocks. Discuss the shapes that have been printed. Patterns made from squares could be used as a wall in a story or rhyme picture, e.g. 'Humpty Dumpty', or the bridge in 'Billy Goat's Gruff'.

Printing shapes

• *Recognising squares and circles*
A piece of sponge soaked in thick paint, paper, empty cardboard rolls, hollow square bricks
Talk to the children about the hollow shapes. Show them how to make prints by pressing the end of a cardboard roll or a hollow brick into the paint-soaked sponge and then onto paper. Ask the children to print patterns with the shapes.

3-d shape

Plasticine shapes

• *Identifying 3-d shapes*
Small assorted 3-d shapes (as in a box of liquorice sweets), Plasticine, blunt knives
Give each child a 3-d shape. (If you use sweets, tell them not to eat them!) Ask them to look carefully at the shape they are holding and to make a similar shape from Plasticine. *Which shapes are easy to make? Why? Which ones are hard to make? Why?*

Make different shapes

• *Identifying 2-d and 3-d shapes*
• *Matching similar 3-d shapes*
Clixi or Polydron
Using Clixi or Polydron, show the children a variety of cubes, cuboids and pyramids. Give them some of the materials to make as many different shapes as they can. Can they name the 2-d shapes that they have used to make the 3-d shapes? Can they match their shapes with yours?

A cone mouse

• *Beginning to recognise shapes*

Thin card, saucers, scissors, sticky tape

Ask the children to draw round a saucer and help them to cut out the circle shape in card. They fold the circle in half and cut to make two semi-circles. Help the children to curve one of the semi-circles into a cone and to stick down the two straight edges. Talk about the shape. *What do you think this shape is called? What does it look like?* They may suggest a witch's hat or an ice-cream cone. Tell them that it is called a 'cone'. The children then cut out strips of card for whiskers and a tail and attach them to their cone. Let them draw on circular eyes and semi-circular ears to complete their cone-shaped mouse.

Cuboid boxes

• *Beginning to discuss flat and curved faces*

A selection of boxes, glue, clothes pegs, adhesive shapes, collage materials, a ramp

Flatten out the boxes along the seams. Give one to each child and ask them to glue the boxes back together again inside out. Use clothes pegs to hold the seams together as they dry. The children can then decorate their box with 2-d shapes, making them into a personality. Suggest that they use circles for eyes, and triangles for noses and mouths. For arms and legs, they could make zig-zag strips and use paper strips or wood shavings for hair. Let them investigate what their characters can do. *Can they be stacked? Will they slide down a ramp? Will they roll down a ramp?*

Roly poly

• *Beginning to discuss flat and curved faces*

A mat, a bench or slide

In a spacious area, challenge the children to make rolling movements on a mat and sliding movements along a bench or a slide. *How are your movements different?* Explain that they roll over all sides of the body, and they slide on one part of the body.